Market Day

a story told with folk art

written and designed by

Lois Ehlert

SCHOLASTIC INC.
New York Toronto London Auckland Sydney
Mexico City New Delhi Hong Kong

Red rooster crows. It's early morn.
Get out of bed.
The chickens
need corn.

Pull up some carrots.
Shake off the dirt.
Pack the tomatoes.
Tuck in your shirt.

Feed the red rooster, turkey, and goose. Lock the gate tight so they won't get loose.

Load up the truck.

We're ready
to go . . .

past the fields where the vegetables

grow,

past the birds
that perch in the trees,
past the snakes
that sun
in the breeze,

past fish and frogs

that swim near the bridge,

and past
the sheep
that graze
on the
ridge.

We're all going
to market.

It's in the
town square.

To buy
and to sell—
that's why
we go there.

Here is the market where we work

and play

till the sun
goes
down
at the
end
of the
day.

Then we load up,
chug over the ridge,

go down the road,
drive over the bridge,

past the trees,
wheels
turning
fast,
past the
fields—

We're home at last.

Let's eat!

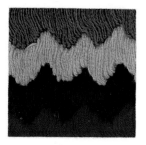

front and back cover
origin: Guatemala
materials: cotton,
embroidery thread

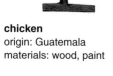

watermelon slice
origin: Mexico
materials: wood, paint
(paper eyes added)

vegetables
origins: Mexico, United States
materials: papier-mâché, paint

chicken
origin: Guatemala
materials: wood, paint

chickens (farm appliqué detail)
origin: Colombia
materials: cloth, thread

house (farm appliqué detail)
origin: Colombia
materials: cloth, thread

baskets
origin: worldwide
materials: fiber, wood

people
origin: Mexico
materials: clay, paint

**goose
(hunting decoy)**
origin: United States
materials: metal,
wood, paint

rooster
origin: Guatemala
materials: wood,
paint

turkey
origin: Guatemala
materials: wood, paint

truck
origin: Mexico
materials: clay, paint

guinea fowl
origin: Africa
materials: wood, paint

dragonfly
origin: China
materials:
wood, paint

cricket
origin: China
materials: reeds

bull
origin: Africa
materials: beads, stuffing

snake (striped)
origin: United States
materials: wood, paint

snake (spotted)
origin: Mali, Africa
materials: wood, woodburned patterns

birds
origin (tan and orange birds): Afri
origin (red bird): India
origin (all others): United States
materials: wood, cloth, beads,
metal, paint

tree (farm appliqué detail)
origin: Colombia
materials: cloth, thread

fruit
origins: Mexi
United State
materials:
papier-mâch

butterfly
origin: Peru
materials: dyed, woven fiber

butterfly
(mola textile detail)
origin: Panama
materials: cotton, thread

cycle
origin: Africa
materials:
discarded metal
containers,
wire, bike
chain, rubber,
plastic

mice dolls
origin: Indonesia
materials: cotton, yarn

ball
origin: Guatemala
materials: cotton, yarn,
stuffing

doll (pre-Columbian)
origin: Peru
materials: wool, cotton,
knitting needles

doll (patchwork)
origin: United States
materials: fiber,
cotton

doll (beaded)
origin: Africa
materials: cloth,
stuffing, seeds,
beads

doll/brush
origin: Mexico
materials: bristles

and frogs
-fishing decoys)
n: United States
erials: wood, metal, paint,
w eyes, beads, tacks, lead in belly

sheep
(farm appliqué detail)
origin: Colombia
materials: cloth, thread

truck
origin: Colombia
materials: clay, paint

flowers
origins: Mexico,
United States
materials: crepe
paper, wire

vegetable market
origin: Peru
materials: cotton, stuffing,
embroidery thread

Ferris wheel
origin: United States
materials: wood, paint,
nuts, bolts

oxen, cart, driver
origin: Mexico
materials: wood, paint, twine

animal (striped)
origin: Mexico
materials: wood,
nails, paint

hearts
origin: Mexico
materials: beads, cotton

doll/purse
origin: Bolivia
material: wool yarn

doll
origin: Mexico
materials: cotton,
wool

textile details
origin: Guatemala
material: cotton

moon/stars
origin: Mexico
materials: tin, paint

rmelon (slice can be removed)
n: Mexico
erials: wood, paint

opossum
origin: Mexico
materials: clay, paint

cart/harness
origin: United States
materials: fiber,
wood, metal

sun
origin: Mexico
material: tin

jaguar
origin: Mexico
materials: wood, paint

Where did they
come from?
What are they
made of?

For Allyn

ISBN 0-439-22356-3

Copyright © 2000 by Lois Ehlert. All rights reserved.
Published by Scholastic Inc., 555 Broadway, New York, NY 10012,
by arrangement with Harcourt, Inc.
SCHOLASTIC and associated logos are trademarks
and/or registered trademarks of Scholastic Inc.

12 11 10 9 8 7 6 5 4 3 2 1   0 1 2 3 4 5/0

Printed in Mexico   49

First Scholastic printing, September 2000

The handmade objects photographed to illustrate this book are from Lois Ehlert's collection, with the following exceptions: the Guatemalan chicken, lent by Allyn Johnston; the Chinese cricket, lent by Pat Ehlert; and the African spotted snake, lent by Dick Ehlert, who also carved the robin, the striped snake, and the red-winged blackbird.

The author made the following elements in order to complete the compositions: embroidery fragments, corn, carrots, cauliflower, the harness and cart for the opossum, and the Ferris wheel.

Photographs by John Nienhuis, Lillian Schultz, and Lois Ehlert

The display type and text type were set in Century Expanded.